BOY, GIRL. BOY, GIRL.

JULES FEIFFER

RANDOM HOUSE   NEW YORK

FOR JUDY

The author wishes to thank The Hall Syndicate, Inc., *The Village Voice,*
Playboy magazine, and *The London Observer* for permission
to reprint the strips in this book.

Published in association with Hall Editions, Inc.

I MEET A GIRL. I TELL HER ALL OF MY MOST INTIMATE PERSONAL SECRETS WHICH SHE PROMISES NEVER TO REPEAT TO ANYBODY. THEN AFTER AWHILE WE BREAK UP.

I MEET ANOTHER GIRL. I TELL HER THINGS ABOUT ME I'VE NEVER REVEALED TO A SOUL WHICH SHE PROMISES NEVER TO REPEAT TO ANYBODY. A COUPLE OF MONTHS LATER WE ALWAYS BREAK UP.

THEN I MEET A NEW GIRL. I EXPOSE MY INNER-MOST FEELINGS TO HER IN A WAY I'VE NEVER QUITE DONE BEFORE — WHICH SHE PROMISES NEVER TO REVEAL TO ANYBODY. SOON IT ALL DIES BETWEEN US AND WE BREAK UP.

.ALL OVER THE CITY
GIRLS WHO NO
LONGER LIKE ME
ARE CASUALLY
WALKING AROUND
WITH MY LIFE'S
CONFESSIONS—

EACH CARRYING AN
INTIMATE PIECE OF ME—
LETTING IT LOOSE TO
GIRL FRIENDS—LETTING
IT SLIP TO NEW BOY
FRIENDS—SPREADING
ME THIN AT PARTIES
ALL OVER TOWN.
THE **WORLD** KNOWS
ABOUT BERNARD
MERGENDIELER!

AND
I'VE
ALWAYS
BEEN
SO
SECRETIVE.

SO RAYMOND TOOK BOTH PHYLLIS AND ME TO THIS RESTAURANT AND HE'S A REGULAR **RIOT**- HE ASKS THE WAITER FOR A GLASS OF WATER.

YEAH? I SAW SOME **GORGEOUS** COTTON BLOUSES TODAY.

YEAH? SO WHEN THE WAITER, ANYHOW, BRINGS THE WATER, RAYMOND - HE'S SO FUNNY I LAUGH WHEN I EVEN **THINK** OF IT - HE TAKES OUT A **NAPKIN** -

YEAH? YOUR SIZE TOO. I WAS **TEMPTED**, I'LL TELL YOU **THAT**. VERY NICE BLOUSES.

YEAH? SO ANYHOW, HE PUTS IT- THE NAPKIN-ON **TOP** OF THE GLASS OF WATER. THEN HE **TURNS** THE GLASS OF WATER OVER ON THE **TABLE**-

YEAH? ACTUALLY, IF I HAD THE MONEY **WITH** ME I WOULD HAVE BOUGHT YOU ONE. YOU NEVER KNOW **WHAT** YOU'RE GOING TO FIND.

PEOPLE FORGET THAT **OURS** WAS THE **FIRST** REVOLUTIONARY COUNTRY! TO WIN THE COLD WAR WE MUST **RETURN** TO THE CONCEPT OF **REVOLUTIONARY** CHANGE.

REVOLUTION! IS ANYBODY LISTENING?

SO WHEN PREVIOUS COLONIAL COUNTRIES BEGIN, AS IT SEEMS THEY **MUST**, TO TOSS OFF THE YOKE OF THEIR OPPRESSORS IT BEHOOVES US TO **TRAIN** OURSELVES TO SUPPORT THEM IN THEIR ASPIRATIONS.

WELL, AS THE PRESIDENT SAID WE **SHOULD** MAKE SACRIFICES.

ONE REALIZES THAT IN THE **FORM-ATIVE** STAGES SUCH A POLICY CHANGE MAY BE MOST **DIFFICULT** SINCE, IN MANY CASES, SAID OPPRESSIVE YOKE IS OFTEN A NATO ALLY OR A NUMBER OF AMERICAN OWNED FRUIT, OIL, SUGAR, MIN-ING, TELEPHONE, OR SOFT DRINK COMPANIES.

YOU'RE EXTREMELY WELL READ, YOU **KNOW** THAT, MARVIN?

HOWEVER WHILE IT MAY BE UN-REALISTIC TO BELIEVE THAT WE WILL CO-OPERATE IN THE EVAC-UATION OF OUR **OWN** CORPORATE WEALTH, IT **IS** COMPLETELY REALISTIC TO **USE** THAT WEALTH FOR TRADING PURPOSES WITH OUR ADVERSARIES.

CLEVER YOU! CLEVER, CLEVER YOU!

FOR INSTANCE, IF WE CAN SWING A DEAL WHERE **WE** OFFER OUR ENEMIES **LAOS, VIETNAM** AND **FORMOSA** - BUT IN RETURN **THEY** MUST TAKE OVER ALL OUR FRUIT, OIL, SUGAR, MINING, TELEPHONE AND SOFT DRINK INTERESTS—\ **THEN** WHEN LATIN AMERICA REBELS IT WILL BE AGAINST **THEM- NOT** US!

NO KIDDING, YOU'RE **BRILLIANT,** YOU KNOW THAT, MARVIN?

BY EXCHANGING AREAS OF EXPLOITATION WE MAY **YET** BE ABLE TO BUILD THE COLD WAR TO A STAND-STILL.

IF PRESIDENT KEN-NEDY COULD HEAR YOU NOW - I **SWEAR** MARVIN, THERE'D **BE** NO ARTHUR SCHLESINGER.

I WAS THE MOST BEAUTIFUL GIRL IN THE NEIGHBORHOOD. I WAS **TERRIBLY** SPOILED.

I WAS ALWAYS THE HANDSOMEST BOY IN SCHOOL. GIRLS **NEVER** LEFT ME ALONE.

IT WAS NO PROBLEM BEING THE CENTER OF ATTENTION. ALL I HAD TO DO WAS TAKE A DEEP BREATH.

I WAS PURSUED BY EVERY FEMALE AROUND. I NEVER HAD TO LIFT A FINGER.

OF COURSE I GREW TO DEPEND ON IT. I CONSIDERED MYSELF **PERFECT**. I BURIED MYSELF IN THE MIRROR.

THEY CALLED ME **LOVER BOY**. I WAS **GAY** AND **COCKY**. I GREW NUMB ABOUT MY CONQUESTS

ALL LIFE OUTSIDE MY OWN BODY BECAME **EXTRANEOUS**. I LOVED ONLY ME. MEN I USED AS A TESTIMONIAL.

BEAUTIFUL GIRLS DID NOTHING FOR ME. **INTELLIGENT** GIRLS DID NOTHING FOR ME. I WAS INVOLVED **ONLY** WITH MYSELF.

LIFE BECAME EMPTY. I **TORTURED** MEN FOR NOT FIGHTING BACK. I WANTED DEMANDS TO BE MADE AND NONE WERE OFFERED.

I GOT TO BE CYNICAL. I HURT GIRLS FOR **KICKS**. I **HUNGERED** TO BE HURT BACK BUT I MET NO ONE EQUIPPED.

THEN I MET YOU.

THEN I MET YOU.

FOR THE **FIRST** TIME IN MY LIFE I WAS ABLE TO FORGET **ME!** IT WAS **ACTUALLY** IMPORTANT HOW **YOU** FELT.

I SUNK MYSELF COMPLETELY INTO YOU. IT WAS AS IF YOU WERE THE ONLY THING IN THIS WORLD I BELIEVED **REAL**.

SO WE **MUST** BREAK UP.

WHO CAN AFFORD THE DANGER?

IT'S ALWAYS BEEN A STRUGGLE FOR ME TO FIND MY PLACE IN SOCIETY. THAT'S WHY I HAVE TO READ BOOKS.

FOR INSTANCE, IN COLLEGE I THOUGHT I WAS GETTING ON FINE, UNTIL I READ THAT MINE WAS A **SILENT GENERATION**. SO I SHUT UP.

AFTER COLLEGE I WENT INTO INDUSTRY AND THOUGHT I WAS DOING FINE, UNTIL I READ THAT I WAS REALLY A **CONFORMIST ORGANIZATION MAN**. SO I WENT OUT AND CONFORMED AND BELONGED.

WELL, I BEGAN MAKING A LOT OF MONEY AND FELT THAT I WAS DOING FINE, UNTIL I READ THAT, IN TRUTH, I WAS A MEMBER OF AN **ACQUISITIVE SOCIETY**. SO I BOUGHT THINGS.

OF COURSE, I NOW HAD A LOT OF TIME ON MY HANDS, BUT I FELT FINE, UNTIL I READ THAT MY INCOME GROUP HAD A **LEISURE PROBLEM**. SO I LEARNED HOBBIES.

NOW FOR A WHILE THERE I FELT FINE, UNTIL I READ THAT THE **ROOT** PROBLEM OF MY AFFLUENT SOCIETY WAS **STATUS SEEK-ING**.

WELL, IN BETWEEN BEING SILENT, CONFORMING, BELONGING, ACQUIRING AND TAKING CARE OF MY LEISURE PROBLEM I HAVEN'T YET HAD A CHANCE TO SEEK STATUS.

I GUESS I'LL FIT IT IN **SOMEHOW**.

I DON'T THINK IT'S ENOUGH TO ATTACK CUBA. I THINK ONE SHOULD LOOK FOR MOTIVATION.

MY OWN FEELING IS THAT THERE'S A BASIC LACK OF EMPATHY. WHY SHOULD **WE** ALWAYS BE EXPECTED TO UNDERSTAND REVOLUTIONARY COUNTRIES? WHY DON'T **THEY** TRY TO UNDERSTAND **US**?

THEY'RE **HOSTILE**. THAT'S WHY. WE'RE LIVING IN A WORLD WHERE REVOLUTIONS HAVE BEEN ABANDONED TO THE UNDER-PRIVILEGED. SHOW ME A REVOLUTION AND I'LL SHOW YOU HOSTILITY TO THE MIDDLE CLASS.

I WAS HOSTILE TO THE MIDDLE CLASS UNTIL I MADE EXECUTIVE LEVEL.

IT'S OUR OWN FAULT! IF THE MIDDLE CLASS SETS THE STANDARDS FOR PEACE TIME WHY SHOULDN'T IT SET THE STANDARDS FOR REVOLUTIONS? IF WE'RE GOING TO WIN THE COLD WAR WE'VE GOT TO INCORPORATE ALL FUTURE REVOLUTIONS WITH MIDDLE CLASS VALUES.

THE ANSWER MAY BE AN EXTENSIVE PRE-REVOLT CAMPAIGN IN ALL EMERGING COUNTRIES— FREE DINER CLUB MEMBERSHIPS — INSTRUCTIONS IN OBTAINING HOME LOANS — MASS AIRLIFTS OF THE READER'S DIGEST.

WE'VE GOT TO CREATE MIDDLE CLASS AMBITIONS— MIDDLE CLASS MYTHS— MIDDLE CLASS HEROES. ONE REASON CASTRO REMAINS SO POPULAR AMONG CUBANS IS BECAUSE THERE'S NO RIVAL TV PROGRAMMING. PUT A QUALITY FAMILY SERIES OPPOSITE HIM AND HE'LL BE **DEAD!**

A TYPICAL CUBAN TELEVISION FAMILY! HOUSE IN THE SUBURBS— TWO CARS IN THE GARAGE — AND A WACKY KID BROTHER WHO LOOKS LIKE RAUL CASTRO!

A CUBAN ANDY HARDY SERIES! — THE IDEAL THAT EVERY CUBAN FAMILY WILL LEARN TO WANT FOR ITSELF!

ONCE WE CAN COUPLE THE INNOCENT ZEAL FOR INDEPENDENCE WITH THE MORE SOPHISTICATED ZEAL FOR INSTALLMENT BUYING OUR FRIENDSHIP WITH THE HAVE-NOT NATIONS IS GUARANTEED.

WE WERE PAYING $65 FOR FIVE ROOMS. ALL RIGHT IT WAS A **SLUM.** I CALL A SPADE A SPADE. BUT I DON'T ASK FOR MUCH. I WAS MODERATELY HAPPY.

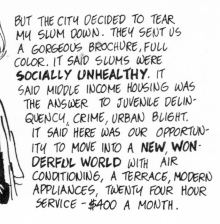

BUT THE CITY DECIDED TO TEAR MY SLUM DOWN. THEY SENT US A GORGEOUS BROCHURE, FULL COLOR. IT SAID SLUMS WERE **SOCIALLY UNHEALTHY.** IT SAID MIDDLE INCOME HOUSING WAS THE ANSWER TO JUVENILE DELINQUENCY, CRIME, URBAN BLIGHT. IT SAID HERE WAS OUR OPPORTUNITY TO MOVE INTO A **NEW, WONDERFUL WORLD** WITH AIR CONDITIONING, A TERRACE, MODERN APPLIANCES, TWENTY FOUR HOUR SERVICE – $400 A MONTH.

WELL, **WE'RE** MIDDLE INCOME. AND WE FIGURED **BUYING** A HOUSE WOULD BE **JUST** AS EXPENSIVE AND **WITHOUT** THE SERVICE. AND **LOOK** WHAT WE'D SAVE ON **COMMUTATION.** SO, IN TWO YEARS, WE MOVED INTO OUR **NEW, SOCIALLY HEALTHY,** MIDDLE INCOME HOUSING.

I DON'T ASK FOR MUCH. TRUE, THE ROOMS WERE A LITTLE SMALLER, BUT THEY DIDN'T LOOK IT BECAUSE THE CEILINGS WERE A LITTLE LOWER. THE TERRACE WAS WHERE OUR OLD FIRE-ESCAPE USED TO BE EXCEPT YOU COULDN'T SIT ON IT WITH THE SOOT BLOWING UP FROM THE MIDDLE INCOME INCINERATOR WHICH ELIMINATED THE NEED FOR NOISY AND CUMBERSOME GARBAGE COLLECTION.

EVERYTIME WE TURNED ON A FAUCET THE WALL BEHIND IT GOT A **WET** STAIN. THE PLUMBING IN THE NEXT APARTMENT WAS **ALMOST** AS LOUD AS THE AIR CONDITIONER IN **OURS**. **SOMETIMES** THE APPLIANCES WORKED. THE TWENTY FOUR HOUR SERVICE **DIDN'T**.

WITHIN A YEAR **EVERYTHING** WAS BREAKING DOWN. THE BUILDERS HAD BEEN IN COURT SIX TIMES OVER AND NOTHING WAS HAPPENING. WE WROTE TO THE CITY TELLING THEM OUR MIDDLE INCOME HOUSING WAS IN DANGER OF BECOMING A **SLUM**.

THE CITY SENT US BACK A GORGEOUS BROCHURE. FULL COLOR. IT SAID SOCIOLOGISTS WERE **NOW** COMING TO BELIEVE THAT SOMETHING **IMPORTANT** HAD BEEN LOST IN THE AREA OF NEIGHBORHOOD INTER-FAMILY GROUP RELATIONS WITH THE BREAKING UP OF SLUMS. IT SAID MIDDLE INCOME HOUSING **LACKED** NEIGHBORHOOD INTER-FAMILY GROUP RELATIONS. IT SAID NEIGHBORHOOD INTER-FAMILY GROUP RELATIONS MAY WELL BE THE ANSWER TO JUVENILE DELINQUENCY, CRIME, URBAN BLIGHT.

SO FOR **NO** SERVICE AND $335 **EXTRA** A MONTH I'M NOW LIVING IN A SOCIAL EXPERIMENT.

IF YOU THINK THIS IS
FUN WHERE WE LIVE
NOW, YOU SHOULD
HAVE BEEN ALIVE
WHERE WE **USED** TO
LIVE **BEFORE** THE
PROJECT.

YEAH?

OH, CERTAINLY, LIKE **NOW**
IN THE MIDDLE OF THE DAY
IF YOU WANT AN **APPLE**
OR SOMETHING, WHAT
DO YOU DO?

AM I
IN THE
PLAY
AREA?

I TAKE A SHORT CUT HOME
THROUGH THE FOUNTAIN
AREA, THE GRASS AREA
AND THE PARKING COLISEUM,
WELL,   THEN I TAKE THE SELF-
O.K.   SERVICE ELEVATOR UP TO
THE NINETEENTH FLOOR,
GO IN THE
HOUSE AND
ASK
MOMMA
FOR
AN
APPLE.

WELL, WHERE WE **USED** TO
LIVE BEFORE YOU WERE
ALIVE, YOU KNOW HOW
I'D GET AN APPLE?

**TELL ME!
TELL ME!**

WELL, I'D STOP PLAYING FOR A MINUTE IN FRONT OF OUR HOUSE WHERE I **ALWAYS** PLAYED AND I'D LOOK UP TO OUR WINDOW AND I'D YELL "MOMMA! COME TO THE WINDOW!

NINETEEN FLOORS?

WELL, WHERE WE USED TO LIVE IT WAS ONLY THE **THIRD** FLOOR. SO ANYHOW MOMMA WOULD COME TO THE WINDOW AND I'D YELL "**THROW ME DOWN AN APPLE, MOMMA!**" AND SHE'D THROW ME DOWN AN APPLE

THROW DOWN AN APPLE? THREE FLOORS?- **OUR** MOMMA?-

WELL, IF YOU LIKE APPLES **NOW** YOU SHOULD TRY THEM AFTER THEY'RE THROWN FROM THE **THIRD** FLOOR.

BOY-

I PITY ALL YOU CHILDREN BORN AFTER SLUM CLEARANCE.

FLORENCE—

YES HENRY—

HOW LONG HAS IT BEEN NOW? SINCE WE WERE MARRIED?

WHAT? SIX YEARS? SEVEN? WHEN EXACTLY WAS IT, HENRY?

LET'S SEE—WAS IT BEFORE OR AFTER "I LOVE LUCY" CAME ON?

I THINK IT WAS BETWEEN "I LOVE LUCY" AND THE "DANNY THOMAS SHOW," HENRY, ISN'T THAT RIGHT?

OH YEAH—BECAUSE I REMEMBER THE NIGHT OF OUR FIRST ANNIVERSARY. I STILL WARM AT THE GLOW OF IT, FLORENCE.

YEAH. MARY MARTIN. "PETER PAN."

AND SHORTLY AFTER THAT OUR LITTLE WENDY WAS BORN.

I REMEMBER— "ALFRED HITCHCOCK PRESENTS"—

THOSE WERE **BEAUTIFUL** YEARS, FLORENCE.

WHERE DO YOU THINK IT BEGAN TO GO **WRONG**, HENRY?

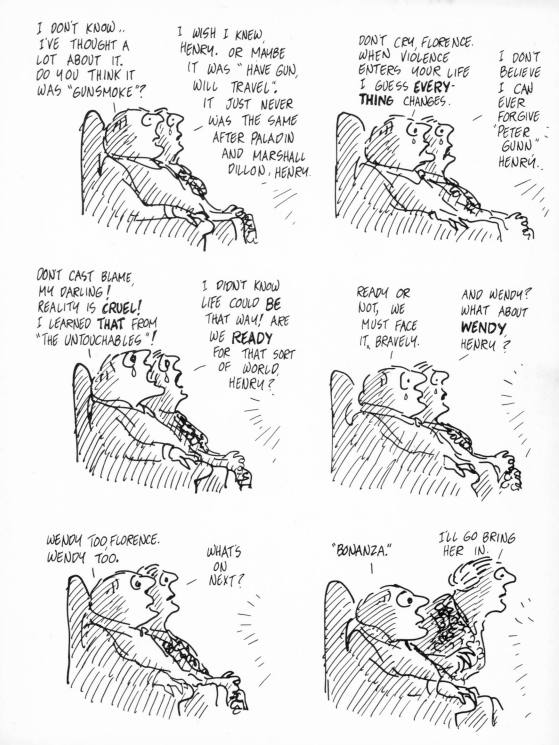

SOMETIMES I WISH I WERE A **DICTATOR**!

A RULER.... A STRONG MAN... A **TITAN** ...

WITH A RUTHLESS GRASP ON POWER AND AN IRON GRIP ON THE HELM OF GOVERNMENT!

—BUT LOVED.

THE LAW IS
MY LAW. THE
PEOPLE ARE
MY PEOPLE.
WHOMEVER
I CONQUER
REMAINS
CONQUERED!

PREMIER BERNARD.
KING BERNARD.
EMPEROR
BERNARD.
CZAR
BERNARD.

BOY.

THEN
COULD
I MEET
GIRLS!

LET'S NOT **AVOID** THE ISSUE, ERNIE. YOU MARRIED ME BECAUSE I REMINDED YOU OF YOUR MOTHER.

I DON'T KNOW WHAT YOU'RE TALKING ABOUT!

AND THAT WAS **ALRIGHT** WITH ME, HONEY. HONEST! YOUR MOTHER WAS A **PLAIN, PLEASANT** WOMAN AND I GUESS THAT'S ALL **I'VE** EVER BEEN.

HAVEN'T YOU EVER HEARD OF **SELF IMPROVEMENT**?

FACE **UP** TO IT, ERNIE! YOU WERE **VERY** SATISFIED WITH ME THE WAY I WAS. IT WAS ONLY WHEN YOUR MOTHER ENROLLED IN **NIGHT** COLLEGE THAT YOU BEGAN TO COMPLAIN.

WHAT'S WRONG WITH A MAN'S MOTHER GOING TO NIGHT COLLEGE?

NOTHING, ERNIE. EXCEPT **HER** INTERESTS AREN'T **MY** INTERESTS ANYMORE. **I** CAN'T TALK WORLD POLITICS THE WAY **SHE** DOES. I CAN'T **SPEAK** FRENCH. **BELIEVE** ME, ERNIE! I **CAN'T!**

REMEMBER YOU SAID ONCE YOU COULD NEVER LEARN TO **DRIVE**

SO **YOU** MADE ME LEARN AFTER YOUR MOTHER GOT **HER** LICENSE. BELIEVE ME, ERNIE, IF **I** FOLLOWED YOUR MOTHER TO COLLEGE SHE'D END UP PRESIDENT OF **HARVARD.** **I** CAN'T COMPETE WITH HER!

MY MOTHER AT LEAST **TRIES.** THAT'S MORE THAN I CAN SAY FOR **SOME** PEOPLE.

ERNIE, IT'S NOT A PLEASANT THING FOR ME TO ADMIT- BUT YOUR MOTHER HAS **OUTGROWN** ME.

I'M SORRY YOU FEEL THAT WAY ABOUT IT, LOUISE.

MOMMA AND I WILL ALWAYS THINK OF YOU AS A FRIEND.

I DECIDED THAT THE WORLD WAS **TOO** MUCH WITH ME AND THAT I NEEDED A PERIOD OF WITHDRAWAL AND REFLECTION

SO I LET MY SUBSCRIPTIONS TO "TIME" AND "THE REPORTER" LAPSE

IN THE BEGINNING THEY BOTH TOOK IT VERY WELL. "TIME" SENT ME SEVERAL REMINDERS ON THE **DUTY** OF THE PUBLIC TO REMAIN INFORMED. "THE REPORTER" SENT ME AN ESSAY BY DE TOCQUEVILLE ON THE AMERICAN CONSCIENCE.

BUT AFTER A FEW WEEKS THE MAIL GOT **HEAVIER**. "TIME" LECTURED ME ABOUT **APATHY** IN THIS YEAR OF PERIL. "THE REPORTER" WROTE THAT THEY COULD NO LONGER IGNORE MY **DELIBERATE** ABSTENTION FROM CIVIC RESPONSIBILITY.

I THOUGHT THE BEST TACTIC WAS NOT TO ANSWER. BUT THIS SEEMED TO AROUSE THEM MORE. "TIME" SENT ME A NUMBER OF STATESMANLIKE MESSAGES FROM MR. LUCE — ABOUT **INDIVIDUALISM**. "THE REPORTER" BEGAN SENDING TWO ISSUES A WEEK AND REGULAR WARNINGS ABOUT THE COLLAPSE OF **LIBERALISM**

BY THE SECOND MONTH I HAD TO HIRE A **SECRETARY** TO HANDLE THE FLOOD OF MAIL. "TIME" WARNED THAT SOON **ALL** MIGHT BE LOST AND IT WOULD BE **MY** FAULT. "THE REPORTER" SENT ME THE COLLECTED WORKS OF JUSTICE FRANKFURTER AND AN URGENT APPEAL TO **THINK**.

WON'T **SOMEBODY** TAKE IT?

IN A **PANIC** I BEGAN
SEEKING THEIR MERCY. I
WROTE THEM THAT I
COULDN'T RE-SUBSCRIBE
BECAUSE OF ILLNESS
IN MY FAMILY AND
SEVERE FINANCIAL
LOSSES IN THE
PAST YEAR.

"THE REPORTER"
SENT ME ITS
VIEWS ON
SOCIALIZED
MEDICINE. "TIME"
WARNED THAT
IT COULD NO
LONGER BE
CONSIDERED
RESPONSIBLE
FOR MY ACTIONS

THEN THE
CUBAN
SITUATION
BLEW UP

THE NEXT MORNING I RE-
CEIVED TWO TELEGRAMS
THE ONE FROM "TIME"
SAID-"DON'T SAY WE
DIDN'T **WARN** YOU "
THE ONE FROM "THE
REPORTER" BLAMED
ME FOR EVERYTHING
AND ASKED FOR THE
RETURN OF ALL ITS
LETTERS

OF COURSE I CALLED THEM
BOTH. "TIME" AGREED TO
REINSTATE ME. "THE
REPORTER" HUNG
UP WHEN THEY
HEARD MY NAME.

ISN'T A MAN
ENTITLED TO
ONE MISTAKE?

I HAVE INNOCENT
LOVE TO GIVE

I HAVE **UNDEMANDING** LOVE TO GIVE. WON'T **SOMEBODY** TAKE IT. \

UNDEMANDING LOVE GIVES ME GUILT FEELINGS. TRY SOMEONE ELSE.

I HAVE EMBITTERED LOVE TO GIVE. LOOK, YOU GONNA TAKE IT OR NOT?
I'VE GOT MY OWN PROBLEMS. BEAT IT!

DO YOU GET NERVOUS WHEN YOU PASS A COP?

OF **COURSE** NOT, HUEY. **SHOULD** I? I MEAN WAS THERE SOMETHING ABOUT THEM I SHOULD HAVE READ?

THE WORLD IS DIVIDED INTO **TWO** CLASSES. THOSE PEOPLE WHO GET NERVOUS WHEN THEY PASS A COP AND THOSE PEOPLE WHO **DON'T**.

OF COURSE **I'M A** OPPOSED TO POLIC BRUTALITY AS **ANYONE** BUT—

NO, BABY- WE'RE NOT TALKING ABOUT **THAT!** WE'RE TALKING ABOUT **POWER**. MY CLASS, BY INSTINCT, KNOWS IT DOESN'T HAVE ANY. YOUR CLASS, BY IN- STINCT, NEVER REALIZED THE QUES- TION WAS AT ISSUE.

YOU'D **LOVE** MY FATHER. HE ALWAYS ENJOYS A GOOD ARGU- MENT OVER POLITICS.

YOU DIG, BABY? WE
E IN **TWO** DIFFERENT
ORLDS. WHEN **YOU**
AR THE WHISTLE BLOW
MEANS **HELP** IS ON
E WAY. WHEN **I**
AR THE WHISTLE
OW IT MEANS
ABOUT TO
T CLOBBERED.

I'VE ALWAYS
BELIEVED IF YOU
HAVEN'T DONE
ANYTHING WRONG
THERE'S NOTHING
TO BE AFRAID
OF.

YEAH? WELL, LET'S SPLIT
OUT OF HERE. GOT ANY
MONEY?

HUEY, HOW
COME **I**
ALWAYS
PAY THE
CHECK?

A PERMANENT VICTIM
REN'T I ENTITLED TO
OME RIGHTS?

I USED TO BE VERY EASILY HURT BY GIRLS. TIME AFTER TIME I'D MEET A GIRL, GET **VERY** INVOLVED AND THEN HEAR HER TELL ME—

"EUGENE, THIS ISN'T WORKING OUT."

SO I'D GO INTO HIDING FOR A MONTH AND READ BOOKS.

AND THEN I'D COME OUT OF MY HOLE AND INTO THE **WORLD** AGAIN. I'D GO TO A PARTY, MEET A GIRL, GET **VERY** INVOLVED AND THEN HEAR HER TELL ME—

"EUGENE, THIS ISN'T WORKING OUT."

WELL YOU CAN SEE WHAT MY PROBLEM WAS— I HAD TO LEARN TO **CONTROL** MY FEELINGS.

SO I STARTED GOING TO PARTIES AND WHEN I'D MEET A GIRL WHO, IN THE PAST I WOULD HAVE AUTOMATICALLY **FLIPPED** OVER — I **IGNORED** HER.

INSTEAD I STARTED GOING OUT WITH GIRLS WHO **DIDN'T** INTEREST ME. GIRLS WHO LIKED **ME** INSTEAD OF ME LIKING **THEM**.

AND WHEN THEY'D GET **VERY** INVOLVED AND THINGS GOT TO BE MESSY AND POSSESSIVE, I'D SAY TO THEM—

"SWEETHEART THIS ISN'T WORKING OUT."

IT'S BEEN OVER A YEAR SINCE I'VE BEEN HURT BY A GIRL.

THESE DAYS I DON'T FEEL A THING.

AND YOU'RE **TERRIBLY** NEAT! YOU'RE MUCH NEATER THAN I EVER CAN BE! AND YOU'RE A **VERY** STRONG WALKER!

AND IF IT WASN'T FOR THOSE TWO YEARS IN THE ARMY I'M **SURE** YOU'D BE MAKING AT **LEAST** AS MUCH MONEY! HONEY, **WHY** GET UPSET?

LARRY! WHAT DO YOU THINK YOU'RE **DOING?**

HEMORRHAGING.

YOU KNOW THE SCENE. I'D MEET SOME **DARL**ING BOY WHO'D BE JUST AS KOOKED UP AS **I** AM. WELL, WE'D MAKE IT TO **MAD** PARTIES FOR A COUPLE OF MONTHS AND **THEN** IT WOULD BE, OF COURSE, **OVER**.

AFTER AWHILE I FOUND IT HARD TO REMEMBER **ONE** FROM THE **NEXT.** I BEGAN TO GET WORRIED ABOUT FINDING SOMEONE **RIGHT** AND SETTLING DOWN. I **AM** NEARLY TWENTY-**SIX** YOU KNOW.

WELL THEN, MY **FA**THER OF COURSE WOULD FLY DOWN AND TELL ME HOW I WAS **DESTROYING** MY MOTHER AND IF I DIDN'T **REFORM** HE'D STOP PAYING MY RENT. **YOU** KNOW THE SCENE— "DON'T USE THAT KIND OF LANGUAGE ON ME, I'M YOUR **FATHER!**" **YOU** KNOW.

AND THOSE SWEET, LITTLE MEN -**HONESTLY**
SWEET- WOULD COME OUT OF THE WOOD-
WORK WANTING TO
GET, OF ALL THINGS,
MARRIED. AND I'D
GET OFFERS, NATURALLY
FOR **JOBS** -MODELLING,
PRIVATE SECRETARY-
YOU KNOW THE
SCENE.

AND ONE OF MY **AUNTS** WOULD (SURPRISE!
SURPRISE!) BE IN TOWN FROM **NOWHERE**
JUST **GASPING** TO BRING
REPORTS BACK HOME.
FINALLY I WAS JUST
EXHAUSTED. I WANT-
ED **FREEDOM** BUT
ALL I GOT WERE
DEMANDS!

SO I SAID THE HELL WITH IT
AND MARRIED WALTER.

I
CAN
USE
THE
VACATION.

IN THE OLD DAYS I USED TO GET INVITED TO THESE PARTIES— YOU KNOW— WHERE THE HOSTESS INSISTED THEY **HAD** TO BE **INTEGRATED**— YOU KNOW? SO THEY'D INVITE **ME.**

AND I'D ALWAYS MEET A WHOLE BUNCH OF OFFICIAL-FRIENDLY PEOPLE— YOU KNOW— **GUYS** WITH **STRONG** HAND SHAKES, **CHICKS** WHO **HAD** TO DANCE WITH ME. IT'S NOT EASY BEING ROBBED OF A CHOICE WHEN THE GIRL IS UGLY.

AND SOONER OR LATER A COUPLE OF THESE CATS WOULD GET ME IN A CORNER AND— WE'D ALL BLOW SMOKE AT EACH OTHER AND BE **ENLIGHTENED**— AND THEY'D WANT TO TALK ABOUT CIVIL RIGHTS UNDER THE DEMOCRATS BECAUSE THERE'S NOTHING A LIBERAL LOVES BETTER THAN BEING MADE TO **FEEL GUILTY**— BUT I WOULDN'T **TOUCH** IT— I'D TALK ABOUT MY **CAR** AND **BASEBALL** AND HOW **DULL** FOREIGN MOVIES ARE.

UNTIL THEY GOT SO JUMPY THAT **ONE** OF THEM **HAD** TO BRING "IT" UP. AND I'D PRETEND TO BE **SURPRISED** THAT THEY'D BE INTERESTED IN **MY** PROBLEMS. BUT THEY INSISTED THAT BEING MEMBERS OF THE **A.D.A.** THEY CON- SIDERED IT **EVERY- BODY'S** PROBLEM.

SO I ONLY SAID I DIDN'T **LOOK ON** CIVIL RIGHTS AS A "**HUMANIST**" ISSUE. THE WAY **I** LOOKED AT IT- IT WAS STRICTLY **SELF-INTEREST.** YOU KNOW—LIKE IT'S BEEN A LONG WAIT AND **I** WANT **MINE.**

SO A COUPLE OF THEM, HERE AND THERE, GOT **RESTLESS** ABOUT WHAT THEY CALLED MY "EXTREMIST" ATTITUDE. BUT ALL THE WHILE THEY KEPT **SMILING.** AS A PEOPLE I FIND LIBERALS VERY **GOOD NATURED.**

BUT THE PARTY ALWAYS BROKE UP ABOUT AN HOUR EARLY AND I COULD SEE **NOBODY** REALLY GOT WHAT THEY **CAME** FOR- EXCEPT **ME.** I FELT I WAS SUBTLY PUSHING A FASTER RATE OF SOCIAL INTEGRATION. AND I WAS **RIGHT.**

AT THEIR NEXT PARTY THEY HAD **TWO** NEGROES— JUST IN CASE THE FIRST ONE DIDN'T WORK OUT.

WHEN MY HUSBAND BEGAN TO BUILD OUR SHELTER HE WAS GOING TO BUILD **TWO** OF THEM. ONE FOR THE FAMILY AND ONE FOR OUR **HIRED GIRL**. SAME DIMENSIONS, SAME MATERIAL, EXACTLY LIKE OURS IN EVERY DETAIL.

WHY NOT. THEY EXPECT YOUR **BLOOD** THESE DAYS.

WELL **YOU** SHOULD HAVE HEARD THAT GIRL TALK WHEN I TOLD HER THE NEWS. I DON'T KNOW **WHERE** SHE PICKED UP SOME OF THE **IDEAS** SHE HAS. SHE'S BEEN WITH US TEN YEARS AND NEVER HAD THEM **BEFORE**.

A LOT OF THEM ARE SECRETLY VERY FRESH.

WELL YOU CAN'T ARGUE WITH A STUBBORN MIND SO WE **GAVE** IN. GOOD GIRLS ARE TOO HARD TO GET THESE DAYS. SO I TOLD HER THAT OUR FAMILY WAS WILLING TO ABIDE BY THE LAW OF THE LAND AND DURING THE NEXT ALERT SHE COULD JOIN US IN OUR SHELTER.

YOU'RE MORE FAIR THAN A LOT OF PEOPLE WOULD 'HAVE BEEN, I'LL TELL YOU **THAT**.

WELL, ON HER DAY OFF A FEW
WEEKS **AFTER** THAT, I
WAS HOME WATCHING THE
U.N. ON TELEVISION -
BECAUSE YOU NEVER
KNOW WHEN ONE OF
THOSE STRANGE
SOUNDING DELEGATES
NAMES IS GOING
TO SHOW UP IN
A CROSS-WORD
PUZZLE.

YOU DON'T
HAVE TO EXPLAIN.
I UNDERSTAND.

AND SUDDENLY THERE **SHE** IS - **OUR** GIRL
AT THE U.N. - **RIOTING!** WELL YOU CAN
IMAGINE I HAD A **FEW** WORDS
READY FOR **HER** WHEN SHE CAME
BACK TO WORK! BUT BEFORE I
COULD OPEN MY MOUTH SHE
SPOKE UP FIRST - SHE HAD
CHANGED HER MIND - SHE
WOULD NOT **SHARE** OUR
IMPERIALIST AIR RAID
SHELTER! SHE WAS NOW
A **NEUTRALIST** AND
WANTED A **SEPARATE**
AIR RAID SHELTER.

WHAT NERVE!
FORCE HER TO
SHARE IT! SHE
CAN'T DO
THAT TO
YOU!

OH, WE TRIED. WE LECTURED HER
ABOUT DEMOCRACY AND QUOTED
ABRAHAM LINCOLN BUT
IN THE END WE HAD TO
BUILD A SHELTER FOR US
AND A SHELTER FOR
HER. GOOD GIRLS
ARE TOO HARD
TO FIND
THESE
DAYS.

THE GOVERNMENT
SHOULD **DO**
SOMETHING. **YOU**
WATCH! **NEXT**
THEY'LL REFUSE
TO GO TO
OUR
SCHOOLS.

SO I WAS SITTING IN THE DARK FEELING VERY RESPONSIBLE BECAUSE WHEN THE SIRENS SOUNDED **I** OBEYED THE LAW AND TOOK SHELTER —

WHEN I REALIZED THAT WE HAD BEEN THERE FOR AN **AWFULLY** LONG TIME. AND SOME OF THE OTHERS WERE BEGINNING TO GROW **RESTLESS**. "THE ALL CLEAR **CERTAINLY** SHOULD HAVE SOUNDED BY NOW SOME PEOPLE SAID.

SO WE FIGURED OUT THE TIME AND IT HAD BEEN OVER FOUR HOURS. SOME OF THE CROWD WANTED TO GO OUT ON THE STREET BUT I'VE ALWAYS BEEN A NATURAL LEADER SO I TOOK CHARGE AND SAID —

"WE TOOK SHELTER BECAUSE THE **LAW** TOLD US TO. IF WE LEAVE OUR SHELTER BEFORE THE **LAW** TELLS US TO, WE AS BAD AS THOSE PEOPLE SITTING OUT IN THE PARK WHO INSIST THIS WHOLE BUSINESS IS INSANE.

EVERYONE AGREED THAT WE CERTAINLY WANTED TO STAY WITHIN THE **LAW**. CALM WAS RESTORED. AFTER TWO MORE HOURS WENT BY A NERVOUS MOTHER SAID — "LISTEN, I'M SURE I HEAR **SOME** MOVEMENT OUT THERE! MAYBE THE SIREN HAS BROKEN."

"**YES**," CRIED EVERYONE. "THE SIREN **MUST** HAVE BROKEN!" BUT **ONCE** MORE I BROUGHT LOGIC TO THE SCENE

I SAID, "THE **LAW** SAYS WE **MUST** WAIT FOR THE SIREN. IF WE LEAVE **BEFORE** WE HEAR THE SIREN EVEN IF IT **IS** BROKEN WE'RE AS BAD AS THOSE PEOPLE SITTING OUT IN THE PARK WHO INSIST THIS WHOLE BUSINESS IS INSANE."

EVERYONE AGREED OF COURSE. WE BEGAN SINGING HYMNS AND RECOUNTING CHILDHOOD EXPERIENCES OF BEING LOCKED IN CLOSETS.

AFTER THE TENTH HOUR THE GROUP WANTED TO SELECT SOMEONE WHO DIDN'T **MIND** BREAKING THE LAW TO GO OUT AND FORAGE FOR FOOD.

SO ONCE **MORE** I HAD TO USE LOGIC. I SIMPLY POINTED OUT THAT SUCH AN ACT WOULD MAKE US **ALL** CONSPIRATORS AND THEREFORE AS **LAW**-DEFIANT AS THOSE PEOPLE SITTING OUT IN THE PARK WHO INSIST THIS WHOLE BUSINESS IS INSANE.

IT'S BEEN THREE DAYS NOW AND THOSE WHO ARE STILL CONSCIOUS ARE BEGINNING TO STIR. PRETTY SOON I'LL HAVE TO SPEAK UP AGAIN.

WITHOUT PROPER RESPECT FOR THE LAW SOCIETY MUST CRUMBLE.

SINCE WE DO NOT FEEL
THERE'D BE SUFFICIENT
OPPORTUNITY TO
CELEBRATE **AFTERWARDS**,
WE OF THE "NATIONAL
DISASTER SOCIETY"
WISH TO PRESENT
OUR **CRASH PROGRAM**
FOR A WORLD WAR III
PRE-CENTENNIAL.

OUR SPONSORS, I AM PLEASED
TO ANNOUNCE, INCLUDE AN
IMPRESSIVE LIST OF GENERALS
ON **ALL** SIDES OF THE IRON
CURTAIN, DEMONSTRATING
ONCE AGAIN THAT CO-EXIST-
ENCE IN TERMS OF EFFECTIVE
ANNIHILATION CONTROL IS A
FEASIBLE AND GROWING
CONCEPT.

PENCILLED IN FOR THE FIRST EVENT IS
A BI-LATERAL PAGEANT TENTATIVELY
TITLED EITHER "DISARMAMENT,"
"**ARMS CONTROL**," OR "**PRE-
EMPTIVE WAR**." IT WILL TRACE,
WITH GRAPHIC FLOATS, THE HISTORY
OF CONCESSIONS BY BOTH SIDES
UNTIL AGREEMENT WAS SO CLOSE
THAT THERE SEEMED NO LOGICAL
WAY OUT BUT TO GO TO WAR.

THIS WILL LAUNCH US INTO THE **WAR GAMES** ASPECT OF OUR PROGRAM—A RE-ENACTMENT OF THE CIVIL WARS IN KOREA, GUATEMALA, LAOS, VIETNAM, CUBA, HUNGARY AND MANY OTHERS — OR, AS IT WILL BE KNOWN IN OUR PROGRAM NOTES—"**OPERATION TIT-FOR-TAT.**" THIS EVENT WILL CONCLUDE WITH A BI-LATERAL TRIBUTE TO AFRICA WHEREIN A LIFE-LIKE FACSIMILE OF THAT CONTINENT WILL BE RE-ASSEMBLED AND BE GIVEN THE PLACE OF HONOR ON THE MAP—WHERE **EUROPE** USED TO BE.

FEELING THE NEED HERE FOR HUMAN INTEREST WE HAVE ASKED DR. TELLER TO GIVE US AN INTIMATE GLANCE OF THE **FAMILY** SIDE OF THE WAR, TO BE ENTITLED, "**MY SON, THE BOMB.**" THIS WILL BE FOLLOWED BY A CALISTHENIC DISPLAY HELD IN THE CITY PARKS BY OUR POLICE DEPART-MENT TO DEMONSTRATE MODERN DETERRENT TECHNIQUES AGAINST OVERT PACIFISM.

MOST OF THE PRESS IS ALREADY CO-OPERATING FULLY AND WE HAVE A PROMISE FROM "LIFE" TO HELP US WITH ALL OUR DISASTERS AS SOON AS IT FULFILLS ITS COMMITMENT TO THE AMERICAN CIVIL WAR.

I MAY BE GUILTY OF OVER-CONFIDENCE, GENTLEMEN, BUT JUDGING FROM INTERNATIONAL RESPONSE, I FEEL THAT THIS YEAR IS **OUR** YEAR.

IRIS, SUGAR!
I'M HOME, DEAR!

HI, NEDDY,
SWEETHEART,
HOW'D IT GO
AT THE UN-
EMPLOYMENT
OFFICE?

NOT SO GOOD, HON BUN.
OLD NEDDY GOT THE
HEAVE HO FOR NON-
DILIGENCE.
WHAT'S
YOUR
NEWS?

NOT SO GOOD
EITHER, LOVER! I
HAVE TO GO TO
DAY CAMP TOMOR-
ROW TO SEE
BARBARA'S ETHNIC
TEACHER. SHE SAYS
BARBARA'S BECOM-
ING A BIGOT!

YOU'D THINK A HOUSE
FULL OF LOVE IS ALL
THE YOUNG WOULD
NEED,
PET!

I KNOW!
DID YOU
CALL THE
TELEPHONE
COMPANY
SWEET?

YES, BABY. THEY SAID THEY WON'T TAKE BACK THE PINK PHONES!

AND I WAS **SO** COUNTING ON THE REFUND MONEY TO BUY FOOD. THE MAN CAME FOR THE SPORTS CAR TODAY, SUGAR!

THAT'S O.K.! I WAS GETTING TIRED OF MOBILITY! DID YOU HEAR FROM THE ARMY, LOVE?

YES! THEY SAID IF YOU RE-ENLISTED NOW THERE'S A GOOD CHANCE YOU CAN HAVE YOUR OLD JOB BACK! BUT THEY COULDN'T GUARANTEE YOU'D BE STATIONED HERE IN SCARSDALE!

HARD NEWS. WELL, FIFTEEN YEARS AND IT'S A FULL CIRCLE, EH, LITTLE GIRL?

IT COULD BE WORSE, DEAR. WE HAVE ALL THAT DISTANCE FROM AFFLUENCE TO SLIDE.

ON THE **FIRST** DATE WE
EXPLODED TOGETHER
LIKE A COUPLE OF
BOMBS. TALKED ABOUT
EVERYTHING! MOST
EXCITING EVENING
OF MY LIFE!

ON THE **SECOND** DATE
WE TALKED HALF THE
NIGHT AWAY DISCUSSING
OUR **FIRST** DATE. SHE
TOLD ME ALL OF **HER**
INSIGHTS ABOUT ME.
I DISCLOSED ALL OF
MINE ABOUT HER.

ON OUR **THIRD** DATE
WE ANALYZED HOW
WE BOTH ACTED ON
OUR **SECOND** DATE—
WHY WE BOTH WERE
A LITTLE **TENSE**—
WHY WE BOTH WERE
AFRAID OF **DISAPPOINT-
MENT.**

ON OUR **FOURTH** DATE
WE EXAMINED CARE-
FULLY ALL THAT
HAD HAPPENED ON
OUR **THIRD** DATE—
THE OBVIOUS
COMPETITIVE-
NESS— THE
GROWING HOSTILITY.

ON OUR **FIFTH** DATE WE SPENT THE NIGHT TAKING APART THE **FOURTH** DATE. SHE POINTED OUT MY SELF PITY AND I PROMISED TO CORRECT IT. I POINTED OUT HER AIR OF DOMINATION. SHE PROMISED TO CORRECT IT.

ON OUR **SIXTH** DATE WE FOCUSED FOR THE COURSE OF THE EVENING ON OUR **FIFTH** DATE- OUR MUTUAL ANXIETY- OUR USE OF SELF EXPOSURE TO KEEP US FROM PHYSICAL CONTACT.

ON OUR **SEVENTH** DATE WE WENT TO A MOVIE. I **LOVED** IT. SHE **HATED** IT. I NEVER REALIZED HOW **INSENSITIVE** SHE WAS.

ON OUR **EIGHTH** DATE I TOOK HER TO A PARTY. MET A **MARVEL-OUS** GIRL! WE EXPLODED TOGETHER LIKE TWO **BOMBS**. MOST **EXCITING** EVENING OF MY LIFE!

SO SHE SAYS NO PERSON HAS THE RIGHT TO TREAT ANOTHER HUMAN BEING LIKE **YOU** TREAT ME.

WELL, SHE **DOES** HAVE A POINT, HUEY. YOUR ACTIONS **WERE** HIGH HANDED.

SO I SAYS, **LOOK**, DON'T **BUG** ME! NOBODY ASKED YOU TO COME OVER.

WELL, **THAT'S** PERFECTLY TRUE. IT **WAS** HER OWN IDEA.

SO SHE SAYS YOU'VE ROBBED ME OF MY DIGNITY. DON'T I MEAN **ANYTHING** TO YOU?

THAT'S CERTAINLY UNDERSTANDABLE. YOU MUST ADMIT THERE **WAS** NO REAL RELATION- SHIP.

SO I SAYS, **LOOK**, DON'T **BUG** ME. I'M LATE FOR CLASS.

I DON'T **KNOW**, HUEY. I GET THE FEELING YOU'RE RATIONALIZING.

YOU SHOULD NEVER HAVE TROUBLE WITH **THEM**, FRAN. YOU SEEM SO FORMIDABLE NO MAN WOULD **EVER** TRY TO PUSH YOU AROUND.

FORMIDABLE? **WHY** DO I SEEM SO FORMIDABLE? BECAUSE ALL OF MY LIFE— DEEP DOWN I FELT LIKE A BLOB OF JELLY.

THAT'S WHY I **COVERED UP**. I WAS SO AFRAID OF BEING HURT I CREATED A VENEER OF **TOUGHNESS**.

YOU?

I NEVER WOULD HAVE BELIEVED IT.

I CHALLENGED MEN BEFORE **THEY** HAD A CHANCE TO CHALLENGE **ME**. IN THE BEGINNING I WAS **AMAZED** HOW EASILY THEY COLLAPSED.

THAT'S WHAT I **MEAN**. BUT FROM YOU THEY ALWAYS WANTED **MORE!**

BABIES. **ALL** BABIES. I KEPT WAITING TO MEET A **REAL** MAN. SOMEONE WHO WOULD CALL **MY** BLUFF. I **KNEW** IF ANYONE CALLED MY BLUFF I'D FALL APART LIKE A BLOB OF JELLY.

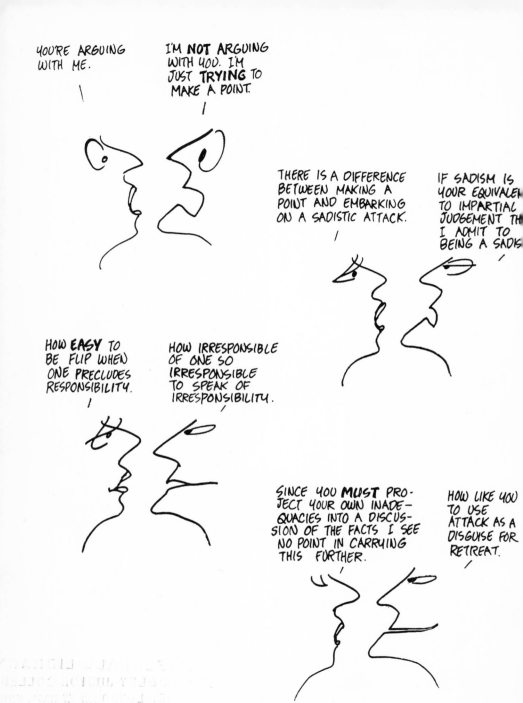

, BUT IF WE'RE NOT ARGUING
YOU SO HEATEDLY CLAIM,
AT IS IT THAT I AM
TREATING FROM?

I'M GETTING
A STOMACH
ACHE.

ME
TOO.

LET'S KNOCK
OFF AND GO
TO A MOVIE.

ALL MY DAYS
ARE SPENT
REWRITING
HISTORY.

WHEN I WAS
AN ADOLESCENT
I WASN'T
HAPPY WITH
MY CHILDHOOD
SO I REWROTE
IT. AND IT SEEMED
A LOT HAPPIER.
WHEN I WAS A
YOUNG MAN I
REWROTE MY
ADOLESCENCE.

I HAD MY FIRST
ROMANCE AT SIX-
TEEN IT TURNED
OUT BADLY. I
REWROTE IT.
I'VE REWRITTEN
EVERY ROMANCE
SINCE – SOME
AFTER FAVORITE
NOVELS, SOME
AFTER SOGGY
MOVIES.

I REWRITE MY
MARRIAGE
CONSTANTLY.
EACH. TIME
IT COMES
OUT A LITTLE
BETTER.
SOME DAY
I MAY HAVE
IT DOWN
PERFECT.

U EXPERIENCES IN
HE MORNING ARE
EWRITTEN TO LOOK
ETTER IN THE
FTERNOON. AT
IGHT I GO
OME, HAVE A
RINK, AND
EWRITE THE
WHOLE DAY.

ANYTHING NEW THAT
HAPPENS TO ME
IS ANALYZED BY
THE KNOWLEDGE
I'VE GAINED
FROM THE
PAST—
REMEMBERED
AS I
REWROTE IT
YEARS AGO.

AT FORTY I AM
APPILY MARRIED
AVE THREE
OVELY
CHILDREN—
A HOME IN
THE SUBURBS—
AND
EXCELLENT
PROSPECTS
FOR JOB
ADVANCEMENT.

NOBODY
KNOWS
IT BUT
I'M A
COMPLETE
WORK
OF
FICTION.

YOU THINK THE END OF THE BLACKLIST IS **GOOD** FOR THE PICTURE BUSINESS? I'LL TELL YOU THE **TRUTH!** IT'S **LOUSY** FOR THE PICTURE BUSINESS. HAVE ANOTHER, EDDIE.

BEFORE THE BLACKLIST WHAT KIND OF MOVIES DID WE MAKE? CLAUDIA AND DAVID MOVIES — "SOMEDAY THERE'LL BE A TOWN HERE, TESSIE" MOVIES — BING CROSBY GOING TO CHURCH MOVIES! CHARLIE, WHATSA MATTER? YOU'RE NOT DRINKING.

QUALITY? **WHAT** QUALITY? MAYBE **ONE** PICTURE EVERY COUPLE OF YEARS. SO **WHAT** HAPPENED? YOU SAY "**TELEVISION**." I SAY "**NOT** TELEVISION." I SAY THE "**BLACKLIST!**" MITCH, YOU'RE SUDDENLY ANTI-SOCIAL? **HAVE** ONE!

THE BLACKLIST WAS THE BEST THING THAT EVER HIT HOLLYWOOD. **WHY**? BECAUSE IT GAVE US "**GUILT.**" BABY, ONCE YOU CHICKEN OUT TO THE AMERICAN LEGION CAN YOU **EVER** BE PROUD AGAIN? HARRY, YOU'RE MAKING ME NERVOUS. ORDER SOMETHING!

ALRIGHT, SO WHAT HAPPENS WITH GUILT? YOU GOT TO GET **RID** OF IT – **BUY** IT OFF – PROVE YOU'RE NOT SUCH BAD GUYS **AFTER** ALL. **THAT'S** WHY WE STARTED MAKING QUALITY PICTURES. ERNIE, **DRINK!**

BECAUSE OF GUILT, PICTURES HAVE BEEN IMPROVING LIKE MAD. THEY GOT SO MUCH INTEGRITY THEY'RE PRACTICALLY **DIRTY.** MILTON, FINISH UP! CHILDREN ARE STARVING IN EUROPE.

SO WHAT DO THESE **IDIOT** PRODUCERS DO? ONE OF THEM WATCHES HIS **OWN** ADULT MOVIE AND DECIDES IT'S MORAL-LY **WRONG** TO HAVE A BLACKLIST. NOW WE'RE **ALL** UP THE CREEK.

ONCE GUILT LEAVES HOLLYWOOD IT'S BACK TO "MY FRIEND FLICKA."

THE ANNUAL MEETING OF THE "**YOU HAVE TO LISTEN TO EXPERIENCE** CLUB" IS NOW IN SESSION. OUR **ACHIEVEMENT** AWARDS THIS YEAR ARE IN THE FIELDS OF PUBLISHING, ADVERTISING AND INDUSTRY.

FOR BEST CONSISTENT CONTRIBUTION IN THE FIELD OF **PUBLISHING** OUR AWARD GOES TO **EDITOR, R.L.K.**, OF THE RECENTLY MERGED FIRM OF **PRENTICE, DOUBLE-HILL, RANDOM** AND **SCHUSTER** FOR HIS UNRIVALLED ALLEGIANCE WITHOUT VARIATION TO THE STATEMENT: "PERSONALLY **I'D** LOVE TO DO IT, WE'D **ALL** LOVE TO DO IT. BUT WE'RE **NOT** GOING TO DO IT. IT'S NOT THE KIND OF BOOK **OUR** HOUSE KNOWS HOW TO HANDLE."
CLAP CLAP CLAP CLAP

OUR SUPERIOR PERFORMANCE AWARD IN THE FIELD OF **ADVERTISING** GOES TO **MEDIA EXECUTIVE, E.L.M.**, OF THE NEWLY CONSOLIDATED FIRM OF **BARTON, RUBICON, WASEY, THOMSON** AND **Y** FOR THE CONTINUALLY CREATIVE USE OF THE OLD FAVORITE: "I THINK WHAT YOU'VE GOT HERE COULD BE VERY EXCITING. WHY NOT GIVE IT ONE MORE TRY BASED ON THE APPROACH **I'VE** OUTLINED AND SEE IF YOU CAN COME UP WITH SOMETHING FRESH."
CLAP CLAP CLAP CLAP CLAP

OUR FINAL AWARD FOR COURAGEOUS HOLDING
ACTION IN THE FIELD OF **INDUSTRY** GOES TO
SUPERVISOR, R.S., OF THE LATELY
AMALGAMATED FIRM OF **CON-EVERYTHING**
FOR HER UNYIELDING GRIP ON - " I
DON'T CARE IF THEY FIRE ME,
I'VE BEEN ARGUING FOR A
NEW APPROACH FOR **YEARS.**
BUT ARE WE **SURE** THAT
THIS IS THE RIGHT TIME—"

CLAP CLAP CLAP CLAP

I WOULD LIKE TO CONCLUDE THIS
MEETING WITH A VERSE WRITTEN
SPECIALLY FOR OUR PROSPECTUS
BY OUR FOUNDING PRESIDENT
FIFTY YEARS AGO - AND NOW,
AS THEN, FULLY EXPRESSIVE
OF THE EMOTION MOST CLOSE
TO ALL OUR HEARTS—

- AHEM -

"TREAT FRESHNESS AS A YOUTHFUL
            QUIRK
AND DARE NOT STRAY TO IDEAS
            NEW,
FOR IF T'WERE TRIED THEY
      MIGHT E'EN WORK
AND FOR A LIVING WHAT
      WOULDST **WE** DO?"

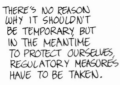

ALL THIS
BIG DEAL
ABOUT
WHITE
COLLAR
CRIME—
WHAT'S
WRONG
WITH WHITE
COLLAR
CRIME?

WHO ENJOYS HIS JOB
TODAY? YOU? ME?
ANYBODY? THE
ONLY SATISFYING
PART OF ANY
JOB IS COFFEE
BREAK, LUNCH
HOUR AND
QUITTING TIME.

YEARS AGO THERE WAS
AT LEAST THE HOPE OF
IMPROVEMENT—EVENTUAL
PROMOTION— MORE
IMPORTANT JOBS TO
COME. ONCE YOU CAN
BE SOLD THE MYTH
THAT YOU MAY MAKE
PRESIDENT OF THE
COMPANY YOU'LL
HARDLY EVER
STEAL STAMPS.

BUT NOBODY BELIEVES HE'S GOING TO BE PRESIDENT ANYMORE. THE MORE PEOPLE CHANGE JOBS THE MORE THEY REALIZE THAT THERE IS A DIRECT CONNECTION BETWEEN WORKING FOR A LIVING AND TOTAL STUPEFYING BOREDOM.

SO WHY **NOT** TAKE REVENGE? YOU'RE NOT GOING TO FIND **ME** KNOCKING A GUY BECAUSE HE PADS AN EXPENSE ACCOUNT AND HIS HOME STATIONERY CARRIES THE COMPANY EMBLEM.

TAKE AWAY CRIME FROM THE WHITE COLLAR WORKER AND YOU WILL ROB HIM OF HIS LAST VESTIGE OF JOB INTEREST.

HI THERE, MR. MERGENDIELER? THIS IS YOUR ELECTRIC COMPANY AND I'LL TELL YOU WHY I'M CALLING, SIR.

YOU MAY REMEMBER A LITTLE WHILE AGO WE SENT YOU A NOTICE THAT OUR METER READER WAS UNABLE TO READ YOUR METER LAST MONTH BECAUSE HE COULD NOT GAIN ADMITTANCE TO YOUR APARTMENT BUILDING? DO YOU REMEMBER THAT MR. MERGENDIELER? **GOOD! GOOD!**

AND WE ASKED IF YOU WOULDN'T **MIND** TAKING A FEW MINUTES OF YOUR TIME TO GO DOWN TO THE BASEMENT AND R[] THE METER FOR US AND F[] OUT THE LITTLE FORM [] SENT ALONG? YOU **DO** REMEMBER? **GOOD!** WE EVEN INCLUDED A STAMP, REMEMBER?

NO, NO, MR. MERGENDIELER, YOU DID **FINE**. YOUR METER READING WAS **PERFECT**. HA. HA. ALMOST LIKE A PROFESSIONAL'S! HA. HA. BUT WHAT I'M CALLING ABOUT IS THE **BILL** FOR $15 YOU INCLUDED FOR SERVICES RENDERED.

NOW YOU MUST UNDERSTAND, SIR, THAT YOUR ELECTRIC COMPANY IS NOT IN THE HABIT OF FARMING OUT **FREE LANCE** WORK. YES, I'M SURE YOUR TIME IS VALUABLE BUT WE THOUGHT YOU MIGHT **NORMALLY** BE TAKING A WALK THROUGH THE BASEMENT ANYWAY — POSSIBLY TO TAKE OUT THE **BABY CARRIAGE** AND ON YOUR WAY YOU COULD **SPARE** THE 30 SECONDS OR SO TO READ THE METER. HA. HA. I SEE. YOU'RE NOT MARRIED.

NO, OF **COURSE** IT'S NOT THE $15 MR. MERGENDIELER. YOUR ELECTRIC COMPANY IS **VERY** SOLVENT. DON'T YOU WATCH OUR WEATHER PROGRAMS? IT'S JUST THAT IF WE PAID A BILL IN **YOUR** CASE WE'D HAVE TO PAY BILLS TO ALL THOSE THOUSANDS OF OTHER PEOPLE IN THE CITY WHO WE'RE ASKING, POSTAGE PAID, TO READ THEIR OWN METERS. THAT **COULD** ADD UP. HA. HA.

SO WHAT IF WE JUST **FORGET** THE $15, MR. MERGENDIELER AND INSTEAD SEND YOU A **LIFE** MEMBERSHIP IN OUR HONORARY **METER MEN OF AMERICA SOCIETY** INCLUDING A LITTLE **METER MAN** BUTTON WITH THE COMPANY EMBLEM ON IT ....

..."PROFIT, WE MUST."

I LIKE YOU VERY MUCH AS A **PERSON**, BERNARD, BUT IT WOULDN'T BE **GOOD** IF WE WENT TOGETHER.

I'M A **VERY STRONG** PERSON. I **NEED** A VERY STRONG PERSON TO GO WITH. I THINK PROBABLY YOU AREN'T THAT STRONG, BERNARD.

I MAKE **IMPOSSIBLE** DEMANDS – YOU HAVE NO IDEA. I'D BE **TESTING** ALL THE TIME – CHALLENGING, DESTROYING.

AND I **KNOW** YOU. YOU DON'T HAVE THE STRENGTH TO FIGHT **BACK**. HOW CAN I COMPETE WITH YOU IF YOU'RE SO WILLING TO ACCEPT DEFEAT?

I NEED A MAN WHO CAN BAT ME **CHALLENGE** FOR **CHAL-LENGE!** I NEED A MAN WH CAN TEST **ME** WHILE I'M TES ING **HIM!** WHO CAN BE MY EQUAL IN DESTRUCTION!

YOU I COULDN'T TEST, BERNARD. AVE TO HIDE MY HOSTILITY, RESS MY AGGRESSIONS, BECOME LE AND **PASSIVE!**

SOON WE'D HAVE NOTHING TO SAY TO EACH OTHER. YOU'D BECOME TERRIBLY BORED.

WE'D HAVE NO CHALLENGE - NO TESTING - NO WINNING - NO LOSING -

COULDN'T WE WORK OUT SOME OTHER INTERESTS?

SO MOMMA AND I GOT ON THIS BUS TO GO TO THE COUNTRY AND SUDDENLY A BUNCH OF COLORED PEOPLE GOT ON AND WE WERE SURROUNDED BY POLICEMEN AND WE ALL GOT ARRESTED.

MOMMA **TRIED** TO TELL THE POLICEMEN WE WERE ONLY GOING TO THE COUNTRY BUT ALL THE COLORED PEOPLE WERE SINGING "**WE SHALL OVERCOME**" SO THE POLICEMEN COULDN'T HEAR US.

SO AFTER DADDY GOT US OUT OF JAIL MOMMA AND I WENT TO GET A **SANDWICH** IN A **DRUG-STORE** BEFORE WE TRIED AGAIN TO GO TO THE COUNTRY—AND SUDDENLY A BUNCH OF COLORED PEOPLE WERE SITTING ON STOOLS ALL AROUND US AND WE WERE SURROUNDED BY POLICEMEN AND WE ALL GOT ARRESTED.

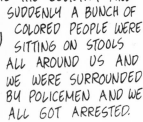

MOMMA **TRIED** TO TELL THE POLICE-MEN WE WERE ONLY TRYING TO **EAT** AND **GO TO THE COUNTRY** BUT ALL THE COLORED PEOPLE WERE SINGING "**WE SHALL OVERCOME**" SO THE POLICEMEN COULDN'T HEAR US.

SO AFTER DADDY GOT US OUT OF JAIL
WE **RENTED** A CAR TO THE COUNTRY
AND MOMMA WAS SO RELIEVED THAT
BEFORE EVEN **UNPACKING** SHE
TOOK ME DOWN TO THE BEACH
TO RELAX AND SUN BATHE
AND SUDDENLY A BUNCH OF
COLORED PEOPLE WERE SUN
BATHING ALL AROUND US AND
THE POLICE MEN CAME AND WE
ALL GOT ARRESTED.

MOMMA **TRIED** TO TELL THE POLICE-
MEN WE WERE ONLY TRYING TO
SUN BATHE BUT ALL THE COLORED
PEOPLE AND ME WERE
SINGING " **WE SHALL
OVERCOME** " SO THEY
TOOK US TO JAIL.

I DON'T MIND THE COLORED
PEOPLE BUT I WISH THEY'D
LEAVE THEIR POLICEMEN HOME.

I'VE ALWAYS THOUGHT
YOU WERE A DEAR,
SWEET BOY, BERNARD.

YOU'RE CONSIDERATE.
YOU'RE FLEXIBLE.
YOU'RE A **LOT** MORE
UNDERSTANDING THAN
I'D EVER BE.

SOMETIMES WHEN I'VE HURT
YOU - YOU GET THAT LOST,
LITTLE BOY LOOK THAT MAKES
ME WANT TO RUN OVER
AND SQUEEZE YOU.

AND LATELY, BERNARD, YOU
HAD THAT LOST, LITTLE BO
LOOK **ALL** THE TIME. I
CAN'T SEEM TO KEEP MY
HANDS **OFF** YOU.

WHY DO I **ALWAYS** WIND UP WITH GIRLS WHO ARE NEUROTIC?

HEY, DIG THAT CHICK IN THE BOOTH. HUH? SOMETHING, HUH? SOMETHING.

I NEVER **KNOW** THEY'RE NEUROTIC IN THE BEGINNING. IN THE BEGINNING THEY SEEM SO **NORMAL**.

SHE'S ON A LITTLE MAG-AZINE KICK. I **LOVE** IT. IT **KILLS** ME.

IN THE BEGINNING THEY TELL ME HOW **KIND** I AM. HOW I'M NOT **CRUDE** AND **DEMAND-ING** LIKE ALL THE **OTHER** MEN THEY'VE MET.

SHE'S LOOKING UP! **WILD** EYES! **WILD**! LOOK **THIS** WAY, BABY!

IN THE BEGINNING WE SEEM TO BE ALMOST THE SAME PEOPLE. WE LOVE THE SAME SONGS- THE SAME MOVIES

SMILE YOU PHON LITTL MAG ZINE CHIC SMI

THEN ALL OF A SUDDEN SHE BEGINS TO HIDE YAWNS WHILE I'M TALKING. WHEN WE'RE ALONE SHE MAKES **LONG** PHONE CALLS.

GO AHEAD! PRETEND TO READ. DON'T PRETEND WITH **ME**, SUGAR. LOOK **UP**! **LOOK** AT ME.

SOON ITS ALL OVER. WE HAVE A LONG CRY ABOUT IT. SHE SAYS ITS ALL **HER** FAULT AND I'M THE ONLY MAN WHO EVER **RE-SPECTED** HER. I'VE LOST A GIRL AND WON A FRIEND.

YEAH. THAT'S MY BABY. LOOK AT THAT NO GOOD LITTLE DOLL SMILE. HEY, LOAN ME A FEW BUCKS, BERNARD.

DO YOU EVER RESPECT GIRLS, HUEY?

IF I HAD ANY RESPECT FOR GIRLS I'D **NEVER** MAKE OUT.

EVERY ONCE IN A WHILE WHEN I'D GET A LITTLE LONELY I'D GO INTO THE NEIGHBORHOOD BAR. YOU UNDERSTAND. JUST FOR A COUPLE OF TALL ONES.

THEN ONE NIGHT I STRIKE UP A CONVERSATION — SOME GUY SITTING NEXT TO ME. HE BUYS ME. I BUY HIM. AND ALL ALONG WE EXCHANGE VIEWS ON **LIFE** —

AND AS WE DRINK HE TRIGGERS OFF IDEAS IN ME I NEVER KNEW I **HAD** AND I CAN SEE I'M TRIGGERING OFF IDEAS IN HIM HE NEVER KNEW **HE** HAD —

AND THE MORE WE DRINK THE MORE **CLEAR** ALL OF LIFE SEEMS TO BE, TILL THE TIME WE FINALLY SPLIT WHEN THE JOINT CLOSES IT'S AS IF **ALL** OF LIFE FOR THE **FIRST** TIME HUNG NEATLY TOGETHER!

THE NEXT DAY, EXCEPT FOR WHERE I GOT MY HEADACHE, I COULDN'T REMEMBER A **THING**.

FOR A COUPLE OF DAYS I WAS VERY DEPRESSED SO I WENT TO THE LOCAL BAR. YOU UNDERSTAND. TO DOWN A COUPLE OF TALL ONES. SOME GUY IS SITTING NEXT TO ME AND WE STRIKE UP A CONVERSATION. HE BUYS ME. I BUY HIM.

AND AS WE TALK AND DOWN DRINKS, ALL SORTS OF IDEAS I NEVER KNEW I HAD **IN** ME ARE EXPLODING IN MY HEAD AND I CAN SEE IT'S THE SAME WAY WITH **HIM**.

AND THE MORE WE BOOZE THE MORE I SEE A WHOLE **CONNECTING PATTERN** OF MY LIFE EMERGING. BY THE TIME WE CLOSED THE JOINT IT WAS LIKE SUDDENLY FOR THE **FIRST** TIME **LIFE** MADE SENSE!

THE NEXT DAY I COULDN'T REMEMBER A **WORD** EITHER OF US SAID. I COULD ONLY REMEMBER ONE THING.

IT WAS THE SAME GUY. IT WAS THE SAME CONVERSATION.

HAVE YOU EVER MET SOMEONE WHO'S NEVER- **NEVER** HAD AN ORIGINAL THOUGHT IN HIS LIFE?

IF YOU ASK ME- IT TAKES ALL KINDS.

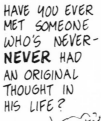

I MEAN SOMEONE WHO IN ALL OF HIS YEARS OF LIVING HAS NEVER UTTERED A WORD THAT WAS UNHACKNEYED OR A SENTENCE THAT WASN'T A CLICHE?

IN MY OPINION, PEOPLE ARE PRETTY MUCH THE SAME THE WORLD OVER.

HAVE YOU EVER HEARD A GUY LIKE THAT ENGAGED IN A **SERIOUS, INTELLECTUAL** DISCUSSION?

WELL, I ALWAYS SAY IT'S A FREE COUNTRY.

AND THE GUY HE'S TALKING TO IS EXACTLY THE WAY **HE** IS - HAVE YOU EVER HEARD SOMETHING LIKE **THAT**?

I LIKE TO THINK THAT WHILE I MAY NOT AGREE WITH WHAT A MAN SAYS-ILL DEFEND HIS RIGHT TO SAY IT.

AND NOBODY IS REALLY SAYING **ANYTHING** BUT EACH THINKS HE'S EXPRESSING **DEEP, PROFOUND** THOUGHTS— I TELL YOU IT'S **DEPRESSING!**

WELL, THIS IS ONLY MY OWN POINT OF VIEW, BUT WHAT ARE YOU GOING TO DO? FIGHT CITY HALL?

WHY DON'T PEOPLE EVER **LISTEN** TO THEMSELVES— WHY DON'T PEOPLE EVER GET **PERSPECTIVE?**

I'VE THOUGHT A LOT ABOUT THAT. I GUESS WE LIVE AND LEARN. WE LIVE AND LEARN.

IF SOME OF US ONLY HAD THE POWER TO SEE OURSELVES AS OTHERS SEE US.

YES— I USED TO FEEL THAT WAY, BUT I OUTGREW IT.

THE COMPANY'S BEEN VERY GOOD TO ME SINCE I GOT OUT OF SCHOOL.

FIRST THEY ENROLLED ME IN THEIR EXECUTIVE TRAINING SQUAD— LEARNING ALL PARTS OF THE FIELD AND GETTING PAID FOR IT AS WELL.

THEN THEY HELPED EVELYN AND ME FIND A HOUSE CONVENIENTLY LOCATED IN A SECTION WHERE **OTHER** YOUNG EXECUTIVES LIVE—

AND WHEN EVELYN BECAME ILL SMACK DAB IN THE MIDDLE OF HER TWENTY FIRST BIRTHDAY PARTY THEY ALLOWED US FULL BENEFIT OF THE COMPANY'S HOSP- ITALIZATION PLAN EVEN **THOUGH** I WAS A MONTH SHORT ON ELIGIBILITY—

—AND IN SPITE OF MY LOW SCORE ON THE MONTHLY PROMOTIONAL EMOTIONAL QUIZ AND SUBSEQUENT DAILY MAKE-UP SESSIONS WITH THE MORALE DEPARTMENT'S PSYCHOANALYST.

THEN WHEN, BECAUSE OF EVELYN'S DRINKING PROBLEM, IT LOOKED LIKE I MIGHT BE CASHIERED, THE EMERGENCY AID COMMITTEE OF THE COMPANY'S FAMILY COUNSELING PLAN PLUS THE WIVES' AUXILIARY'S "BE A PAL" SERVICE HELPED PULL US THROUGH.

NOW THE LITTLE WOMAN AND I ARE BACK IN STEP. HERE I AM ONLY TWENTY-FOUR AND ALREADY A SECOND CONSULTATION ASSISTANT. AND JUST YESTERDAY EVELYN ENROLLED OUR THREE-YEAR-OLD IN THE EXECUTIVE JUNIORS TRAINING SQUAD.

I COULD DIE FOR THE COMPANY.

I FOUND
A FLOWER!

I FOUND
A
FLOWER!

1

MY FLOWER IS BIG
AND BEAUTIFUL AND
EXTREMELY ROBUST.

THAT'S
TRUE.

YOUR FLOWER
IS DARK AND
UNGAINLY AND
MAY NOT LIVE
TILL MORNING.

IT WILL
CERTAINLY
BE A
STRUGGLE.

YOU SEE WHAT THE PROBLEM **IS**, A LOT OF THESE **NEW** COUNTRIES ARE COLORED AND THEY'RE—YOU **KNOW**—VERY OVER SENSITIVE.

BOY, DON'T I **KNOW!** YOU SHOULD SPEAK TO THE GIRL I HAVE COME IN ON MONDAYS.

AND I DON'T HAVE TO TELL YOU THE WAY IT IS— THEY DON'T HAVE OUR WEALTH OF **EXPERIENCE**—I MEAN BASICALLY THEY'RE A VERY **INNOCENT** PEOPLE—I MEAN—**THEY'RE** NOT SOPHISTICATED!

WELL, YOU'RE EITHER OR YOU'RE NOT I SAY.

THEN THEY COME TO THE UNITED NATIONS IN NEW YORK AND THEY EXPECT EVERYBODY TO BE THEIR **FRIEND**. THEY DON'T UNDERSTAND ABOUT NEW YORK. NOBODY'S **ANYBODY'S** FRIEND.

CAN YOU **IMAGINE**? THEY'RE VERY INNOCENT IF YOU ASK ME.

SO IF THEY GET TREATED NASTY IN A RESTAURANT OR FOR INSTANCE GET SHOVED IN THE STREET THEY THINK ITS BECAUSE WE DON'T **RESPECT** THEM.

WELL I'VE DISCOVERED AFTER A LONG LIFE THAT YOU HAVE TO **EARN** RESPECT. IF YOU'RE NOT IN **TOO** MUCH OF A HURRY — IF YOU KNOW YOUR PL —

BUT YOU DON'T UNDER-**STAND!** DON'T YOU SEE THEY ALL HAVE CHIPS ON THEIR SHOULDER! SO NOW IT LOOKS LIKE IF WE DON'T SERVE THEM NICE IN OUR RESTAURANTS, THEY'LL ALL GO COMMUNIST.

COMMUNIST! AND I USED TO THINK THEY WERE ALL SO GOOD-NATURED. WELL YOU TURN YOUR BACK ON PEOPLE FOR A MINUTE AND —

SO RATHER THAN LET THEM GO COMMUNIST I SUPPOSE ITS OUR DUTY TO HELP THEM — BUT AFTER ALL ITS A HARD LIFE FOR **EVERYBODY.** I MY-SELF DON'T ALWAYS GET THE BEST SERVICE IN RESTAURANTS. BUT **I'M** A GOOD SPORT. I LAUGH IT OFF.

AFRICA WOULD BE A LOT BETTER OFF IF IT WAS MORE LIKE YOU, DORIS.

FOR A SOCIETY—**ANY** SOCIETY—
TO FUNCTION PROPERLY IT
NEEDS **OUTLETS**-**RELEASES**.
IT NEEDS **ENTERTAINMENT**
AND **DIVERTING TRIVIA**.
IN OUR SOCIETY FOR
ENTERTAINMENT WE
HAVE **THEATRE**, WE
HAVE **MOVIES**, WE
HAVE **TV**.

FOR
DIVERTING
TRIVIA
WE
HAVE
A
FREE
PRESS.

THE FUNCTION OF A FREE PRESS,
AS WE KNOW IT, IS NOT TO
PUBLISH **ALL** THE NEWS. WHO'D
READ IT? IT'S NOT EVEN TO
PUBLISH THE TRUTH. WHO'D
KNOW IT? THE FUNCTION
OF A FREE PRESS IS TO
PUBLISH FREE PRESS
RELEASES.

THUS IF A RELIABLE PENTAGON
SOURCE LEAKS AN ANTI-DISARMAMENT
STORY ALL THE ANTI-DISARMAMENT
PRESS WILL PLAY IT UP **BIG**
WHILE THE **PRO**-DISARMAMENT
PRESS (WHAT THERE IS OF IT)
WILL BURY IT ON PAGE
FORTY.

IF A RELIABLE JUSTICE DEPARTMENT
RCE LEAKS A PRESS RELEASE ON
E NEW **ANTI-MONOPOLY** PROSE-
ON, THE ANTI-MONOPOLY PRESS
AT THERE IS OF IT) WILL PLAY
P BIG WHILE THE **PRO-**
OPOLY PRESS WILL BURY
N PAGE FORTY TILL
CAN TIE IT TO
RESS RELEASE ON
NEXT **JIMMY HOFFA**
ECUTION.

IF A CRITIC OF THE STATE IS
JAILED BEHIND THE IRON CURTAIN
OUR PRESS WILL PUBLISH SELF-
RIGHTEOUS EDITORIALS DENOUNC-
ING ALL POLITICAL PERSECUTION.

IF A CRITIC OF A CONGRESSIONAL
COMMITTEE IS JAILED **OVER
HERE** OUR PRESS WILL
PUBLISH SELF RIGHTEOUS EDIT-
ORIALS PROCLAIMING THAT
FREE SPEECH DOESN'T GIVE
ANYONE THE RIGHT TO CRY
"FIRE" IN A CROWDED THEATRE.

PAPER HAS ITS
LINE AND STICKS
. EVERY PAPER
ITS OWN PROS-
US—" ALL THE
THATS SAFE
RINT"—AND
TICKS TO
T.

FREE
PRESS?
WE'RE A
NATION
OF
TRADE
JOURNALS.

OU'RE ABSOLUTELY
RCEPTIVE ABOUT
E. GOD, I'M **REALLY**
OCENTRIC. LOOK, I
M INEXHAUST—
LY SORRY!
HAT ELSE
AN I TELL
OU?

NOTHING I SAY HAS
THE SLIGHTEST
EFFECT.
WELL, ARE
YOU TAK-
ING ME
TO
DINNER
OR
AREN'T
YOU?

GOD, I ONLY WISH I **COULD**
BUT I'M MEETING SOME—
BODY IN ABOUT **FIVE**
MINUTES.
GOD, I'M
SO EM-
BARRASSED
ADMITTING
THIS.

YOU SIMPLY
AMAZE
ME,
STEVIE.

LOOK— I MADE A TERRIBLE ERROR BUT
I'M WILLING TO SET IT RIGHT.
I DON'T CARE **WHAT** THE
GIRL I'M
MEETING
THINKS.
WHY DON'T
YOU GET
YOURSELF
A DATE
AND
JOIN
US!

IN THE
BEGINNING
I WANTED
TO BE A
SINGER.
I SANG
ALL THE
TIME.

BUT EVERYONE
TOLD ME I WAS
UNREALISTIC.
MOST SINGERS
NEVER GOT
ANYWHERE. SO
I GAVE IT UP.

THEN I TOOK
TO WRITING
POETRY. I
LOVED
WRITING
POETRY. I
DID IT DAY.
AND NIGHT.

BUT EVERYONE
TOLD ME I WAS
UNREALISTIC.
MOST POETS
DIED **BROKE.**
SO I GAVE
IT UP.

LATER ON I DEVELOPED A PASSION FOR **PAINTING**. I PAINTED EVERY MINUTE OF THE DAY.

BUT EVERYONE TOLD ME I WAS **UNREALISTIC**. IT TOOK **YEARS** TO MAKE PAINTING PAY OFF. SO I GAVE IT UP.

NOW I'M AN ACCOUNTANT.

BUT I SING TO MYSELF IN THE SHOWER AND WRITE POETRY IN MY HEAD ON THE BUS AND READ ARTICLES ON ART EVERY SUNDAY IN THE PAPERS.

EVERYONE SAYS I'M A REALIST.

MY FIRST PAPERBACK TITLE WAS "THE **NAKED SLASHER PENTHOUSE** CAPER". THE JACKET WAS IN **BLOOD RED** WITH THE DRAWING OF A CHAINED, HALF NAKED GIRL HOLDING A KNIFE AT THE THROAT OF A PRIVATE COP IN A TRENCH COAT.

THE SUB-HEAD ON THE COVER WENT— "WHEN THE SEDUCTRESS FROM THE SANITARIUM HIRED DETECTIVE MIKE YESTERDAY ALL THE RULES HAD TO BE REWRITTEN."

IT WENT FOR TWENTY-FIVE CENTS. IT SOLD TWELVE MILLION. I HAD FIFTEEN PAPERBACKS AFTER THAT— BING! BING! BING! TWELVE MILLION! TWELVE MILLION! TWELVE MILLION!

THEN— ALL OF A SUDDEN— **NOWHERE!** PRICES GO UP, HOT COVERS GO OUT, **CLASS** COMES IN. I CAN'T EVEN GET AN EDITOR TO **TALK** TO ME.

SO LAST YEAR I GOT **WITH** IT! MY **NEW** BOOK CAME OUT UNDER THE TITLE "**FUNCTIONAL ASPECTS OF THE MORAL DICHOTOMY IN JUDEO-CHRISTIAN MAN**" THERE'S A PAINTING OF MOZART BY BEN SHAHN ON THE COVER!

AND ONLY WHEN YOU TURN TO THE INSIDE DO YOU SEE THE **SUB-HEAD** — "WHEN THE SEDUCTRESS FROM ANTIOCH HIRED ANTHROPOLOGIST MIKE YESTERDAY ALL OF DESCARTES' THEORIES DEMANDED REAPPRAISAL." AND JUST UNDER THAT IT READS — "A CRITICAL ALLEGORY OF OUR TIME."

IT'S SOLD FOURTEEN MILLION COPIES, I'VE GOTTEN DOZENS OF OFFERS TO SPEAK AT UNIVERSITIES, AND "OMNIBUS" IS DOING MY LIFE STORY.

THE HALLMARK OF A PROFESSIONAL IS A PROFOUND KNOWLEGE OF HIS MARKET.

TALK
DIRTY.

TALK
DIRTY?

NOT SELF-CONSCIOUS DIRTY
LIKE ITS A CURRENT IN-THING
SHE DOES THAT HERSELF.
I MEAN **ANIMAL** DIRTY.
LIKE YOU GOT TO MAKE
HER BELIEVE SHE'S IN
A **JUNGLE** AND THE
RULES SHE LEARNED
IN SCHOOL **DON'T**
WORK!

TALK DIRTY?
YOU **REALLY**
MEAN TALK
DIRTY?

MAKE AN URBAN CHICK
FEEL DEFENSELESS AND
SHE'LL CONFUSE IT
WITH **LOVE**.
WITH ALL THAT
ARMOR WHERE
COULD SHE
GET THE
EXPERIENCE TO
KNOW THE
DIFFERENCE?

THIS
WORKS?

MAN - TALK DIRTY, NEVER PAY
A CHECK AND TAKE HER
TO TENNESSEE WILLIAMS
PLAYS - IT **HAS** TO
WORK. TO THE
URBAN CHICK
BRUTALITY
IS A
STATUS
SYMBOL.

I USED TO SEND ESSAYS TO THE FEUDAL BARONS ON LAND REFORM. FOR MY EFFORTS THEY WOULD TOSS ME IN THE DUNGEONS AND BEAT ME.

I USED TO PETITION THE CLERGY ON THE SINFULNESS OF SACRIFICIAL RITES. FOR MY EFFORTS THEY TOSSED ME IN THE DUNGEONS AND BEAT ME.

I USED TO PREPARE MANIFESTOS FOR THE MERCHANTS ON THEIR ABUSES OF THE POOR. FOR MY EFFORTS THEY WOULD SIC THEIR DOGS ON ME AND BEAT ME.

BUT SOON A MORE ENLIGHTENED TIME CAME. MY COUNTRY PROSPERED WITH RICH HARVESTS AND FRUITFUL COMMERCE. A NEW SPIRIT WAS ALLOWED FREE IN THE LAND!

I AGAIN SENT MY ESSAY ON LAND REFORM TO THE BARONS. THE BARONS LOVED IT! THEY ASKED ME TO ENTERTAIN WITH LECTURES AT EACH FORE-CLOSURE.

I RESUBMITTED MY PETITION AGAINST SACRIFICES TO THE CLERGY. THE CLERGY DEVOURED IT! IT WAS WIDELY DISCUSSED AT EVERY SUBSEQUENT SACRIFICE.

I REDISTRIBUTED MY MANIFESTOS ON THE ABUSES OF THE POOR TO THE MERCHANTS. THE MERCHANTS WERE ECSTATIC! THEY ASKED ME TO FORM A FACT-FINDING COMMITTEE.

THAT WAS ALL A LONG WHILE AGO. I AM STILL AT WORK WHILE BEING LAVISHLY SUPPORTED BY THE BARONS, THE MERCHANTS AND THE CLERGY WHO POINT AT ME AS A SYMBOL OF THEIR DEMOCRATIC INSTINCTS.

IF SUPPRESSION CAN NOT DIS-ARM CRITICISM, AMIABLE ACCEPTANCE **CAN.**

1-29

A DANCE TO
THE LOSS
OF
INNOCENCE.

IN THIS DANCE I
HAVE SYMBOLIZED
YOUTH,
ITS HOPES,
ITS WISHES,
ITS DREAMS,
ITS CHOICE
OF FRIENDS,
OF LOVERS,
OF GODS.

YOUTH - BRIGHT AND
EAGER TO
SEARCH
LIFE FOR
ITS MEAN-
ING -
CERTAIN
IN THE
KNOWLEDGE
THAT IT
WILL
FIND THAT
MEANING.

AND THEN
COMES
DISILLUSION.

THE DISAPPOINTMENT
OF FRIENDS —
THE INADE-
QUACY OF
LOVERS —
THE FAILURE
OF GODS.

THE GAINING
OF BITTER
INSIGHTS —
THERE IS
NO ONE WHO
DOESN'T LIE —
THERE IS
NOTHING
INCORRUPTIBLE.

THEY'RE ALL
CHEATS
AND OUT
TO GET YOU!
DON'T BE-
LIEVE A
SINGLE
ONE OF
THE NO
GOOD
DIRTY —

FORGET
IT —

I DON'T **FEEL** LIKE DANCING.

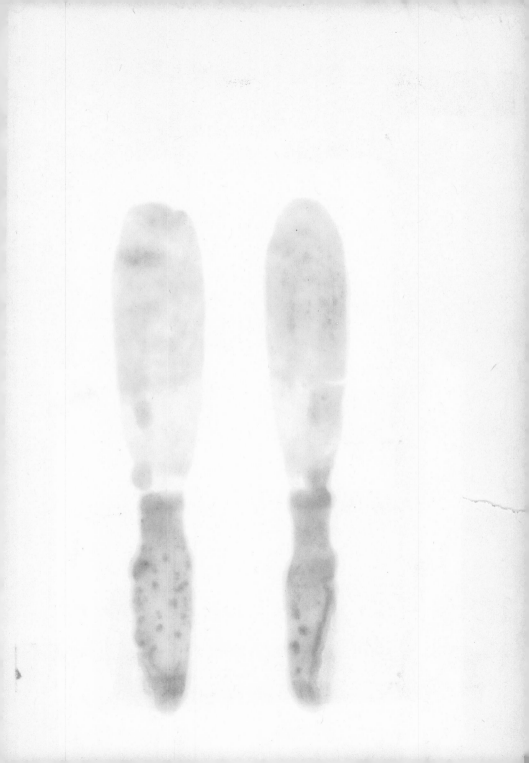

DATE DUE

GAYLORD   PRINTED IN U.S.A.